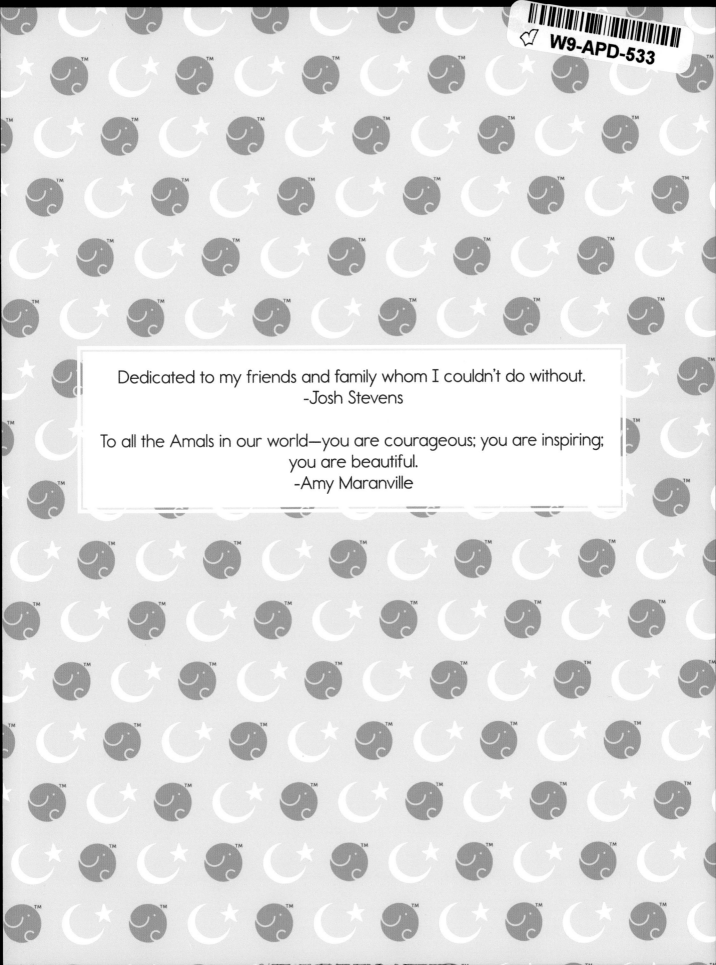

Dedicated to my friends and family whom I couldn't do without.
-Josh Stevens

To all the Amals in our world—you are courageous; you are inspiring;
you are beautiful.
-Amy Maranville

Amal's Ramadan
Story by Amy Maranville   Art by Joshua Stevens

www.bharatbabies.com

Amal's Ramadan

For more information, please contact:
Mascot Books | 560 Herndon Parkway #120 | Herndon, VA 20170
info@mascotbooks.com

Library of Congress Control Number: 2016904321

CPSIA Code: PRT0516A
ISBN-13: 978-1-63177-745-5

Printed in the United States

Early one summer morning, before the sun peeked over the edge of the horizon, my mother pressed her hand gently to my shoulder to wake me.

"Amal," she said, "it's time to eat."

Careful not to wake my brother Youssef, I climbed down the ladder from my bunk bed, thumped down the stairs, and found my family in the kitchen. The table was set for *suhoor*, the morning meal of Ramadan. "Good morning, Amal," said my nana. "Good morning, everyone," I said, rubbing my eyes.

My mother put a bowl in front of me, filled with *haleem*. Haleem is a creamy wheat porridge topped with lamb meat. It's a breakfast that helps keep us full all day. I scooped a big spoonful and smiled as the familiar flavor woke me up. *Mmmm.*

During Ramadan, Muslim families like mine don't eat or drink when the sun is in the sky. We also pray and try to be better people.

When I was younger, like my brother Youssef, my parents said I was too small to do the fast. I had to concentrate in school and needed lots of food and water.

So I would pray with my family and look forward to Eid, the celebration at the end of Ramadan, when my grandparents come and we all eat together.

But at twelve years old, I was old enough to try to do a full fast. I was so excited!

As we finished our *suhoor* on that first morning, my parents spent time explaining the importance of paying attention to my body.

"Sometimes being hungry can make you feel dizzy," my mother said.

"Sometimes it can make you grumpy or sad," my father said.

"So make sure you tell your counselor if you don't feel like yourself," said my mother.

In the warm morning light of our family kitchen, all their advice seemed silly. I would be fine.

At first, everything was fine. My father dropped my brother and me at summer camp, reminding me to "let someone know if you aren't feeling well."

I ran around with my friends, went swimming, and made a birdhouse with lots of blue sparkles.

At lunch I was hungry, but also excited to get my first chance to fast. "Why aren't you eating, Amal?" my friend Kenya asked.

"I'm Muslim," I told her, "and during Ramadan, we don't eat when the sun is out."

"What, all day?" my friend Charlie asked.

"Yup," I said proudly. "All day."

"Wow, you must be soooo hungry," said Kenya, biting into one of her cookies.

The cookie looked good. It had chocolate chips and coconut flakes. For a second, I really wanted to ask Kenya if I could have one. But then I remembered and felt happy that I didn't ask for a cookie.

Soon, lunch was over. "Let's play tag," Kenya said.

"Great idea!" said Charlie. "I'll be it!"

We chased each other, laughing. Then all of a sudden…

My head started spinning. I tried to keep running, but I only got dizzier.

At first, I was scared and confused. But then I remembered what my parents said. I went to my counselor and told her I didn't feel well.

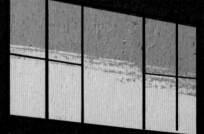

The counselor made me go to the camp nurse. I was afraid. Would they make me break my fast? The nurse called my mother, and she asked to talk to me. "Amal, my chēlē, what is wrong?

I started crying. "I feel dizzy, Mama."

"Oh sweetie, don't cry. Remember, we told you that your first fast can be hard."

"I don't want to stop fasting," I sniffled.

"I know, my love, I know."

My mother asked the nurse to give me some cranberry juice. Usually, Muslims don't drink during the day when they are fasting. I felt ashamed as I drank the small cup of juice. My head felt better, but my heart felt heavy.

That night, my family gathered for *iftar*, the evening meal during Ramadan. Delightful smells wafted from the kitchen. My nose told me that curry with chick peas, onion pakoras, porota pancakes, and lemon rice would soon appear.

As the sun set, my parents passed out cups of juice and sweet dates to help us ready our stomachs for food.

"Amal, how was your first day fasting?" my father asked.

"He had to drink juice," Youssef said, his mouth full of dates.

I looked down at my lap, trying not to cry. I had been so sure of myself, but fasting was harder than I thought.

"Amal, don't be sad," my noni said kindly. "I had to break my fast the first time, too."

"You—you did?"

"Me too," my nana said. "Fasting is very hard. The important thing is that you tried, and you took care of yourself. You will only get better at it."

Before bed that night, my family hugged me close. "We're so proud of you, Amal."

I was proud of myself, too.

And tomorrow, I would try again.

Pronunciation Guide

Hi friends, you might notice that our pronunciation guide is a little different from other guides. We use familiar words to make pronunciations easier and more accessible. We hope this helps you learn more about the amazing cultures, religions, and people from India.

Amal - *a-maal*
Main character of the Amal's series

Youseff - *you-sef*
Amal's mischievous little brother

Suhoor - *sue-who-r*
The pre-dawn meal had before sunrise during the holy month of Ramadan

Ramadan - *raam-a-daan*
The holy month of fasting, introspection, and prayer observed by Muslims around the world

Nana - *naa-naa*
Bengali for grandfather

Haleem - *haa-lee-m*
A hearty dish of barley, lentils, and ground meat

Eid - *ee-d*
The celebratory festival held to mark the end of Ramadan

Pakoras - *paa-koo-raa-s*
A deep fried savory snack

Porota - *po-roo-taa*
A thick, multi-layer, piece of unlevened flatbread

Iftar - *if-taa-r*
The meal eaten after fast is broken during Ramadan